Rive WILD

CONTENTS

My White-Water River Rafting Trip

Written by Terry Miller Shannon

Photographed by Andy and Angie Belcher

The trip hadn't started. But I was sure it was another one of my father's lame ideas.

Dad's camera

My life vest

Our guide, Leaf, told us how to stay safe.

We kept things dry in waterproof bags or boxes.

Dad was excited.

I still wished I was home playing video games.

Even I had to admit it.

The view was OK.

Pine and oak trees grew along the river.

A rainbow stretched over one of the waterfalls.

We rode tons of rapids.
Rapids are parts of the river
where the water moves quickly.
If a rapid is rated 1, it is as tame as the bath.
If it's rated 5, it's the wildest ride.
Some rapids have names,
such as Wildcat and the Bone Cruncher.
Our wildest rapids were rated 3.
They were like the wettest, coldest, and most exciting
roller-coaster rides!

Wild Animals We Saw

An osprey (OSPRAY)
is a huge hawk.
It swoops down
to snatch fish.
Its nest can be
over 1.8 metres wide.

We watched a beaver
build a dam.
A beaver's dam
is made of sticks,
mud, and rocks.

A mother deer
and her babies ate
grass along the river.
A baby deer
is called a fawn.

A bald eagle circled high in the sky. It's not really bald. It just has white feathers on its head.

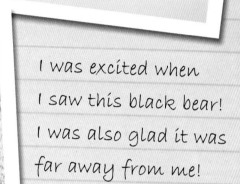

I was excited when I saw this black bear! I was also glad it was far away from me!

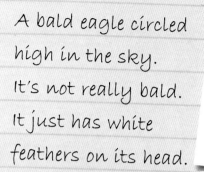

What other animals might you find near a river?

7

Waterfalls make
the best slides!

Home, sweet campsite!
We camped for a night
on the river bank
before finishing our trip downriver.
We told stories around the campfire.
I counted shooting stars until I fell asleep.

Here I am at the end of our trip.
I'm saying,
"Dad, when can we go on
another white-water rafting trip?"

How else could this story have ended?

Talking with a

Written by Terry Miller Shannon

This is Leaf. He has been a river guide for many years.

Q. How do you become a river guide?

A. You can go to a river guide school
or a trained river guide can teach you.
You must take many trips with skilled guides.

River Guide

PHOTOGRAPHED BY ANDY & ANGIE BELCHER

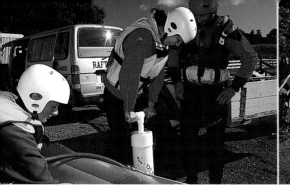

Q. Is becoming a river guide hard?

A. Yes. There's a lot to learn.
Guide students must know
how to stay safe in water.
They learn how to judge river conditions.
They practise piloting the raft
through the rapids.
They learn how to cook outside
and how to avoid harming the outdoors.
Guide students also learn the names
of animals and plants.
And they take classes in first aid.

Q. Have you ever had any unusual animal encounters?

A. One night in camp,
I woke up to find a warm body
cuddled up next to me.
That snuggler was a skunk!

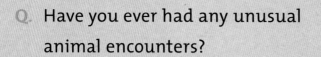

Once, I saw some deer
swimming through rapids.
At the end of the rapids,
they got out and
walked up the river bank.
Then those fun-loving deer swam
down the rapids again!

14

Q. What's the best part of being a guide?

A. My whole job is an adventure.
I can't pick a favourite part!
I enjoy watching wildlife.
I like working outside.
I like sharing my love of nature.
This is the perfect job for me!

What kind of person would make a good river guide?

Riverkeepers

Written by Barbara Diamond

Illustrated by Alan Cochrane

Green River

SCHOOL NEWS

October 15

Students Adopt Green River

By Isabella Santos for Mr. Kim's Class

Mr. Kim's class has adopted part of the Green River.
Yesterday we visited the river and picked up rubbish.
We also took water samples.
The samples will tell us if the water is polluted.

Ms. Johns, "the Riverkeeper", helped us.
She told us that we are all riverkeepers.
She works for the Fishermen's Group.
She helps clean up the pollution in the river.
She makes sure people keep the river clean.

Green River in Danger?

By Isabella Santos for Mr. Kim's Class

Mr. Kim's class is on alert!
A class member may have spotted a river polluter.

Early yesterday, Tony Favaza was fishing
with his grandmother on the Green River.
They went past a big oil tanker.
They heard the captain talking by radio.

"Captain of the *Southern Star* here," he said.
"We are dumping all our sea water.
Then we will clean out our tanks.
Don't take on any fresh water now."

CRYSTAL
LAKE

OCEAN

Southern Star

GREEN RIVER

What else could Mr. Kim's class do to help clean up the river?

Tony wondered whether the captain
was allowed to do that.
He saw the *Southern Star* dumping sea water.
He took some water samples to give to Ms. Johns.

Look for more on this story in a few days.

Green River

Water Samples Prove Pollution

By Isabella Santos for Mr. Kim's Class

The *Southern Star* poisoned our river.
Ms. Johns tested the water samples.
They had high levels of toxic chemicals.
"These chemicals could end up in our
drinking water," Ms. Johns said.

Ms. Johns found out the *Southern Star* carries
oil for the Oasis Oil Company.
After it delivers the oil,
it fills its empty tanks with sea water.
Then the boat comes up our river.
Here it dumps out the sea water.
The water has toxic chemicals in it.
They are left over from the oil.

"Tankers should not dump toxic water in our river.
We must ring the Oasis Oil Company.
We must tell them to stop," Ms. Johns said.

Meanwhile, Mr. Kim's class keeps taking water samples. They may need them to prove Oasis Oil is polluting the river!

An Oil Tanker

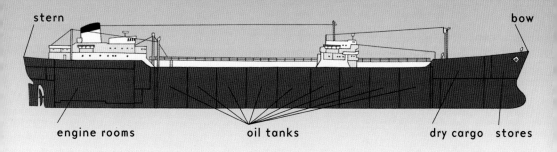

stern

bow

engine rooms   oil tanks   dry cargo   stores

When the tanks are not full of oil, they hold sea water or fresh water. The tanks are filled and emptied carefully to keep the tanker balanced.

Oasis Oil Will Stop Polluting!

By Isabella Santos for Mr. Kim's Class

Oasis Oil has agreed to stop dumping toxic water into the Green River.
They will also give money to the Fishermen's Group.
The money will be used to help clean up our river.

Mr. Kim's class has been busy.
The students found out that 20 other tankers also dumped sea water into the Green River.
Mr. Kim's class took more than 120 water samples from the water around the tankers.
The samples proved that the tankers were dumping toxic water.

"I'd like to thank the students of Mr. Kim's class for joining this fight to save our river,"
Ms. Johns told reporters at a news conference.
"They are all riverkeepers now."

The Scent of a River

Written by Laura Hirschfield

Does every river have a special smell?
If you could ask a salmon,
it would say, "Yes!"

Salmon are born in rivers and streams.
But young salmon don't stay
in their river homes for long.
When they are about one year old,
they leave the river and head
for the ocean.
They swim a long way.
As they swim,
their bodies change
so they can live in the salty ocean water.

When young salmon
begin swimming to the ocean,
they are called smolts.

Why do you think salmon go back to the river?

Salmon stay in the ocean
for one to seven years.
They swim, eat, and grow.

After a few years in the ocean,
it is time for the salmon to go home.
They go back to the exact rivers
and streams where they were born.
How do they find their way back?
They remember the way
their river homes smelled!

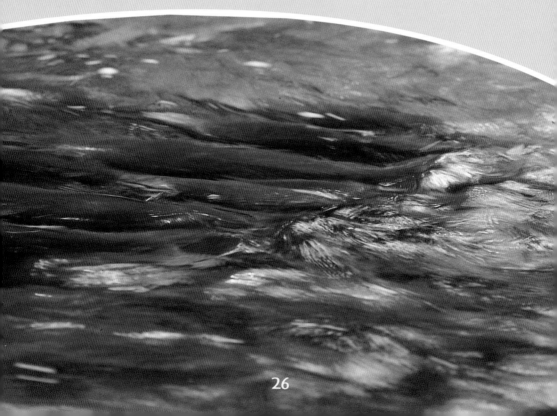

26

These salmon can grow 1.8 metres long.
They can weigh over 57 kilograms!
They're called king salmon.

Salmon smell through small nostrils. Scientists are still learning about the salmon's sense of smell.

It is a long and dangerous journey.

Dams and waterfalls get in their way.

Fishermen try to catch the salmon.

Bears, seals, and other animals try to eat them.

Once the salmon leave the ocean,

they will not stop to eat or rest.

The journey may take several months.

Some will not make it home.

People have made special fish
ladders to help salmon
swim over dams.

28

Some salmon turn bright red or green when they travel home. They change colour to attract a mate.

Finally, the strongest salmon
find the river where they were born.
There, female salmon
dig nests in the river bed
by swishing their tail back and forth.
Inside the nests,
they lay their eggs.

A female salmon can lay up to 17,000 eggs!

eggs

When salmon babies are born,
the cycle starts all over again.
The babies learn the smell of their river homes.
One day, they will go to the ocean.
And, one day, they will smell their way back home.

Life Cycle of a Salmon

A salmon looks very different at each stage of its life.
Each stage has a name.

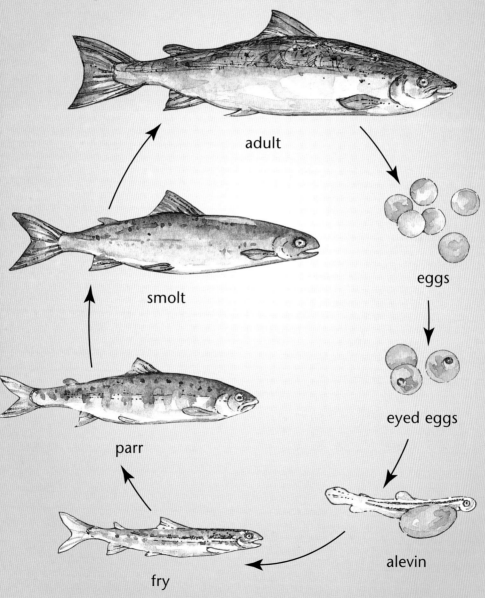

adult

smolt

eggs

parr

eyed eggs

fry

alevin

Index